Good Science—*That's Easy*

 M000101132

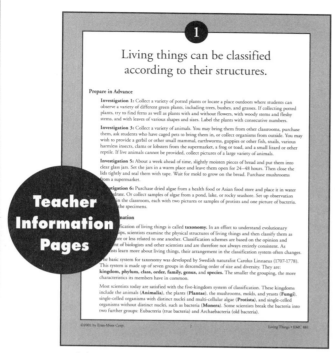

- the concept to be studied
- items to obtain or prepare in advance
- background information

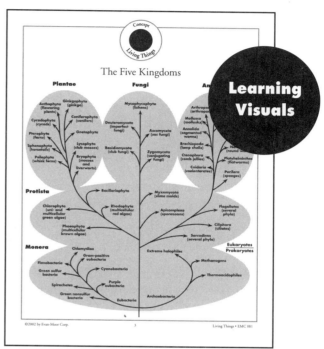

- reproduce or make into a transparency

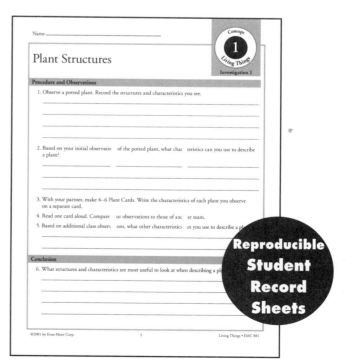

Living things can be classified according to their structures.

Prepare in Advance

Investigation 1: Collect a variety of potted plants or locate a place outdoors where students can observe a variety of different green plants, including trees, bushes, and grasses. If collecting potted plants, try to find ferns as well as plants with and without flowers, with woody stems and fleshy stems, and with leaves of various shapes and sizes. Label the plants with consecutive numbers.

Investigation 3: Collect a variety of animals. You may bring them from other classrooms, purchase them, ask students who have caged pets to bring them in, or collect organisms from outside. You may wish to provide a gerbil or other small mammal, earthworms, guppies or other fish, snails, various harmless insects, clams or lobsters from the supermarket, a frog or toad, and a small lizard or other reptile. If live animals cannot be provided, collect pictures of a large variety of animals.

Investigation 5: About a week ahead of time, slightly moisten pieces of bread and put them into clear glass jars. Set the jars in a warm place and leave them open for 24 to 48 hours. Then close the lids tightly and seal them with tape. Wait for mold to grow on the bread. Purchase mushrooms from a supermarket.

Investigation 6: Purchase dried algae from a health food or Asian food store and place it in water to rehydrate. Or collect samples of algae from a pond, lake, or rocky seashore. Set up observation stations in the classroom, each with two pictures or samples of protists and one picture of bacteria. Number the specimens.

Teacher Information

The classification of living things is called **taxonomy.** In an effort to understand evolutionary relationships, scientists examine the physical structures of living things and then classify them as being more or less related to one another. Classification schemes are based on the opinion and judgment of biologists and other scientists, and are therefore not always entirely consistent. As scientists learn more about living things, their arrangement in the classification system often changes.

The basic system for taxonomy was developed by Swedish naturalist Carolus Linnaeus (1707–1778). This system is made up of seven groups in descending order of size and diversity. They are: **kingdom, phylum, class, order, family, genus,** and **species.** The smaller the grouping, the more characteristics its members have in common.

Most scientists today are satisfied with the five-kingdom system of classification. These kingdoms include the animals (**Animalia**); the plants (**Plantae**); the mushrooms, molds, and yeasts (**Fungi**); single-celled organisms with distinct nuclei (eukaryotes) and multicellular algae (**Protista**); and single-celled organisms without distinct nuclei (prokaryotes), such as bacteria (**Monera**). Some scientists break the bacteria into two further groups: Eubacteria (true bacteria) and Archaebacteria (old bacteria).

The Five Kingdoms

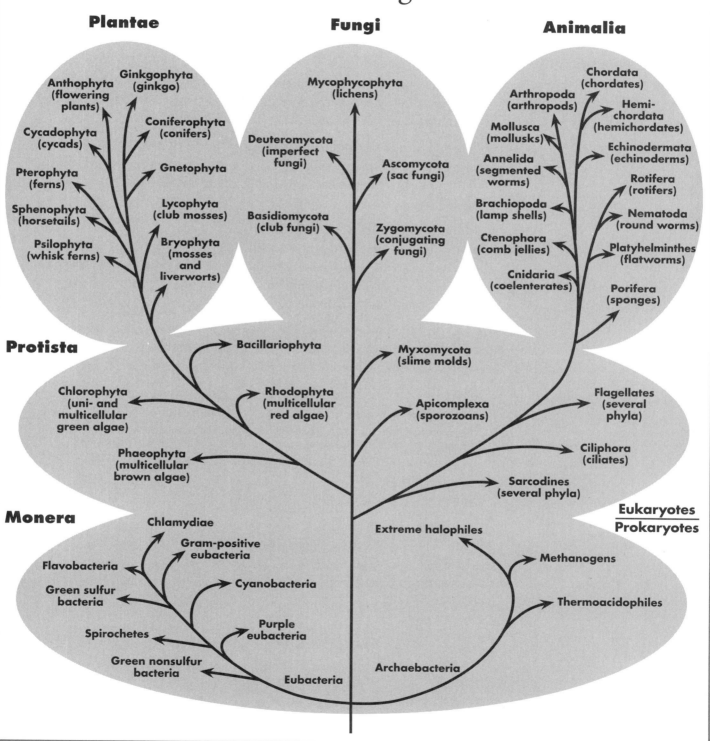

Plantae

Anthophyta (flowering plants)
Ginkgophyta (ginkgo)
Coniferophyta (conifers)
Cycadophyta (cycads)
Gnetophyta
Pterophyta (ferns)
Lycophyta (club mosses)
Sphenophyta (horsetails)
Bryophyta (mosses and liverworts)
Psilophyta (whisk ferns)

Fungi

Mycophycophyta (lichens)
Deuteromycota (imperfect fungi)
Ascomycota (sac fungi)
Basidiomycota (club fungi)
Zygomycota (conjugating fungi)

Animalia

Chordata (chordates)
Arthropoda (arthropods)
Hemichordata (hemichordates)
Mollusca (mollusks)
Echinodermata (echinoderms)
Annelida (segmented worms)
Rotifera (rotifers)
Brachiopoda (lamp shells)
Nematoda (round worms)
Ctenophora (comb jellies)
Platyhelminthes (flatworms)
Cnidaria (coelenterates)
Porifera (sponges)

Protista

Bacillariophyta
Myxomycota (slime molds)
Chlorophyta (uni- and multicellular green algae)
Rhodophyta (multicellular red algae)
Apicomplexa (sporozoans)
Flagellates (several phyla)
Phaeophyta (multicellular brown algae)
Ciliphora (ciliates)
Sarcodines (several phyla)

Eukaryotes
Prokaryotes

Monera

Chlamydiae
Gram-positive eubacteria
Flavobacteria
Green sulfur bacteria
Cyanobacteria
Spirochetes
Purple eubacteria
Green nonsulfur bacteria
Eubacteria
Extreme halophiles
Methanogens
Thermoacidophiles
Archaebacteria

Concept 1 Living Things

Investigation 1

Plant Structures

Materials

See advance preparation on page 2.

- student record sheet on page 5, reproduced for each student
- potted plants, various kinds
- index cards

Steps to Follow

1. Set out a potted plant. Invite students to describe its physical structures. Write their observations on the board.

2. Challenge students to use the list on the board to define characteristics they could use to describe any plant (for example, oblong leaves = shape of leaves, fleshy stem = type of stem). Record these characteristics on the board and have students record them on their record sheets.

3. Display a variety of potted plants or take students outside to an area with a variety of different plants. Make sure the plants are identified with consecutive numbers. Give each team of two students four to six index cards.

4. Have students create Plant Cards. Tell each team to observe four to six different plants. Using the class list, they should note each plant's characteristics and record this information on a card, along with the number of the plant. Have each group observe at least one plant that another group is also observing.

5. Invite one team to read aloud the observations they wrote on one plant card. Have other teams read their observations of the same plant. Invite students to discuss the similarities and differences in their observations. Repeat this with other teams.

6. Have students look again at the list of characteristics on the board. Invite them to add new characteristics to the list, based on their more extensive observations.

Follow-Up

Ask students what characteristics they think scientists use to describe plants. Provide field identification guides. Have students list the characteristics used in the books. Compare this list to the class list. Discuss which characteristics are most important to look at when identifying plants.

Name _____

Plant Structures

Procedure and Observations

1. Observe a potted plant. Record the structures and characteristics you see.

   _____

   _____

   _____

   _____

2. Based on your initial observations of the potted plant, what characteristics can you use to describe a plant?

   _____ _____ _____

   _____ _____ _____

   _____ _____ _____

3. With your partner, make four to six Plant Cards. Write the characteristics of each plant you observe on a separate card.

4. Read one card aloud. Compare your observations to those of another team.

5. Based on additional class observations, what other characteristics can you use to describe a plant?

   _____ _____ _____

   _____ _____ _____

Conclusion

6. What structures and characteristics are most useful to look at when describing a plant?

   _____

   _____

   _____

   _____

Investigation 2

Classifying Plants

Materials

- student record sheet on page 7, reproduced for each student
- Plant Cards from Investigation 1

Steps to Follow

1. Explain to students that scientists **classify,** or group, organisms based on similar characteristics. Divide students into pairs. Have each team study their Plant Cards. Have them divide the plants they observed into two groups, based on similar structures. Tell them to identify a characteristic, such as thorns, that some plants have and others do not. Based on this, have them separate the cards into two groups: the plants in one group have the characteristic, and those in the other do not.

2. Challenge students to divide each group of plants a second time. Remind them that all plants in a group must share a characteristic. Explain to students that they may use a different characteristic to divide each group. Tell them to record how they decided to group the plants.

3. Have three to four teams form a group. Have them lay out all their Plant Cards on the floor. Challenge them to use the same method to separate the plants into groups based on similar structures. Have them begin with two large groups. Then challenge students to separate the plants into smaller and smaller groups.

4. Allow time for students to view how other groups separated their Plant Cards. Discuss similarities and differences in the characteristics they used to form their groups.

Follow-Up

Provide students with a dichotomous key to the identification of plants. Discuss similarities and differences between the characteristics used in the key and those identified by students.

Classifying Plants

Procedure and Observations

1. Divide your Plant Cards into two groups. What characteristic did you use?

_____

2. Divide each group into two smaller groups. What characteristics did you use?

_____

3. Form a larger group by joining together with two to three other teams. In the large group, work together to separate your Plant Cards into two groups. What characteristic did you use?

_____

4. Compare the plants in the two groups. How are they alike? How are they different?

_____

_____

5. Divide each large group of Plant Cards into smaller and smaller groups. What characteristics did you use to further separate the plants?

_____

_____

6. Compare the characteristics of the plants in one small group with the characteristics of the plants in the two large groups. Record your observations.

_____

_____

Conclusion

7. How did observations of plant structures help you separate plants into groups?

_____

_____

_____

Investigation 3

Animals All Around

Materials

See advance preparation on page 2.

- student record sheet on page 9, reproduced for each student
- variety of living animals, or pictures of animals
- fish net (optional)
- reclosable plastic bags
- tweezers
- hand lenses
- index cards

Steps to Follow

1. Invite students to observe the characteristics of an animal they are familiar with—the human being. Record their observations on the board.

2. Challenge students to use the list they have made to decide what characteristics they might look for when observing other kinds of animals, for example, number and type of limbs, type of outer covering (scales, skin, fur, hair, etc.). Have students write these ideas on their record sheets.

3. Give each team of two students four to six index cards and a hand lens. Provide a variety of animals or pictures of animals to observe, or take students on a collecting and observing field trip. Have each team observe four to six different animals and make Animal Cards. Using their list of characteristics to look for, they should note each animal's characteristics and record this data on a card. Try to have teams observe a variety of animals.

4. Invite one team to read aloud the observations they wrote on one Animal Card. Based on the characteristics, challenge the other students to point out the animal being described. Give each team a turn.

5. Discuss what made it easy or hard to identify an animal based on its description.

Follow-Up

Provide field identification guides. Have students list the characteristics used in the books to identify animals. Compare this list to the class list. Discuss which characteristics would be most useful in identifying an animal.

Discuss how students knew that the organisms they observed were alive.

Animals All Around

Procedure and Observations

1. Observe the human animal. List its characteristics.

   _____

   _____

   _____

   _____

2. What characteristics might you look for when observing an animal?

   _____   _____   _____

   _____   _____   _____

   _____   _____   _____

3. Observe four to six different animals. Make Animal Cards to show the characteristics of each one.

4. What characteristics did you actually look at when observing animals?

   _____   _____   _____

   _____   _____   _____

   _____   _____   _____

5. Read aloud one of your cards. Challenge other students to identify the animal you described.

Conclusion

6. Why is it important to base the description of an animal on accurate observations?

   _____

   _____

   _____

   _____

Investigation 4

Classifying Animals

Materials

- student record sheet on page 11, reproduced for each student
- Animal Cards from Investigation 3
- large manila envelope

Steps to Follow

1. Review the method students used in Investigation 2 to divide plants into groups. Invite students to comment on this method.

2. Have students work in teams of four, using their Animal Cards from Investigation 3. Two students will perform the task described below while the other two students respond orally.

3. Instruct two students in each group to work together to identify a characteristic that some of the animals have but others do not, such as wings. Tell them to put all the Animal Cards that do *not* have this characteristic in the envelope without telling the others what the characteristic is. Have them record the characteristic on their record sheets and then challenge the other two students to identify the characteristic they used by looking at the remaining cards.

4. Using the remaining cards, have the same two students choose another characteristic that some of the animals have and others do not. Follow the same procedure as before.

5. Instruct students to repeat the process until only one card remains. Using the characteristics they identified, invite students to describe the last remaining animal. Have them evaluate the usefulness of this set of characteristics for identifying this animal.

6. Switch roles so that the pair who did the guessing is now dividing the cards and keeping track on their record sheets. They will repeat the process starting with a different characteristic to divide the cards into two groups. Discuss how this affects their results.

7. Have volunteers explain how they classified the animals. Challenge students to compare and contrast the different ways they separated the animals.

Follow-Up

Ask students what would happen during the classification process if two groups observed the same animal but made different observations. Discuss the importance of accurate observations to the process of classification.

Concept

1

Living Things

Investigation 4

Classifying Animals

Procedure and Observations

1. Work with a partner.

2. Combine your team with another team. There should be four students in your group. Observe all the Animal Cards. Find a characteristic that some animals have and others do not. Put the Animal Cards that do *not* show this characteristic into the envelope. In space "a," write the characteristic that separated the two groups. The other pair of students on your team will try to identify the characteristic you used.

   a. Animals with _____

3. Divide the remaining Animal Cards again. Record the characteristic you used.

   b. Animals with _____

4. Keep dividing the cards until only one remains. Each time, record the characteristic you used. Add more spaces if you need them.

   c. Animals with _____

   d. Animals with _____

   e. Animals with _____

5. Describe the last remaining animal, based on the way you classified it.

   _____

   _____

6. Switch roles with the other pair. They will sort the cards and record on their record sheets the characteristics they used to do so. Then you and your partner will try to identify the characteristics they used.

Conclusion

7. How can you classify animals based on their physical characteristics?

   _____

   _____

   _____

Investigation 5

Neither Plant Nor Animal

Materials

See advance preparation on page 2.

- student record sheet on page 13, reproduced for each student
- plastic cups
- sugar
- warm water
- teaspoons
- yeast packets
- mushrooms
- mold cultures
- hand lenses

Steps to Follow

1. Tell students that they will now investigate another large group of living things known as **fungi** (singular, **fungus**). Explain that fungi are neither plants nor animals. Review some of the characteristics of plants and animals. Explain that fungi cannot make their own food as plants can. They get their food from other organisms as animals do. But unlike animals, they cannot move.

2. To prepare a yeast culture, tell students to fill a plastic cup half full with warm water, add the packet of yeast and 1 spoonful of sugar, and stir. They should let the mixture sit for about 5 minutes.

3. Give each team a mold culture in a sealed glass jar and a mushroom. Have students observe the yeast, mold, and mushroom both with the naked eye and with the hand lens. ***Caution: Students should not open the mold culture jars for any reason.*** Make sure they record their observations on their record sheets.

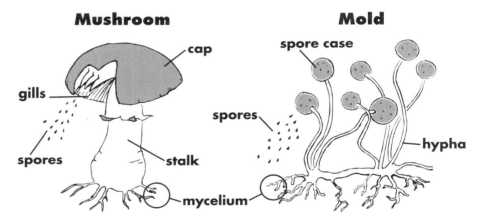

Follow-Up

Provide students with field identification guides to fungi. Have them compare the characteristics used to identify fungi in the books with those they noticed in the fungi they observed. Discuss characteristics found throughout.

Invite someone from a local mycological club, college, or university to speak to the students about mycology (the study of fungi).

Invite parents to prepare mushroom dishes and bring them to class for a tasting party. This exercise is especially rewarding if dishes from various cultures are shared.

Neither Plant Nor Animal

Procedure and Observations

1. Make a yeast culture by mixing warm water, sugar, and dry yeast. Wait 5 minutes.

2. Observe the yeast, the mushroom, and the mold. Use your hand lens. Record your observations.

	Mushroom	Mold	Yeast
What color is it?			
Does it move? If so, how?			
What plant-like structures does it have?			
What animal-like structures does it have?			
What else do you notice?			

3. How are fungi similar to plants? How are they different?

_____

_____

4. How are fungi similar to animals? How are they different?

_____

_____

Conclusion

5. Why do you think scientists classify fungi in their own kingdom?

_____

_____

Investigation 6

Too Small to See

Materials

See advance preparation on page 2.

- student record sheet on page 15, reproduced for each student
- pictures of various protists and bacteria
- living or dried algae
- books with pictures and descriptions of protists and bacteria

Steps to Follow

1. Tell students they will now make observations of organisms from the Protist Kingdom and the Kingdom Monera (Bacteria). Explain that bacteria are the smallest living things. Provide students with a variety of pictures of **protists** and **bacteria** (singular, **bacterium**). Discuss the characteristics of each group.

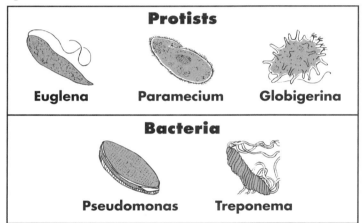

2. Prepare observation stations, each with two pictures or samples of protists and one picture of bacteria. Label each sample with a consecutive number. Point out which pictures were taken through a microscope and the degree of magnification used.

3. Invite students to view the pictures and samples at three stations. Have them write their observations on their record sheets.

4. Assign each team to one of the stations at which they made observations. Challenge them to decide which organisms are bacteria and which are protists. (Bacteria have no distinct nuclei, while protists do.)

5. Have the class group all the pictures to show their decisions. Discuss the differences between protists and bacteria.

Follow-Up

Collect and culture pond water. Keep it in a warm place out of direct sunlight. Provide microscopes and hand scopes. Have students observe samples of water and locate various protists.

Obtain books from the library that describe the features of bacteria and protists. Have students compare these descriptions to their own observations.

Name ____________________

Concept 1 Living Things

Investigation 6

Too Small to See

Procedure and Observations

1. Look at the pictures and samples at each station. Record your observations on the chart below.
2. Are the organisms at your station bacteria or protists? Record your ideas.

Organism #	Observations

Organism #	Bacteria or Protist?	How Did You Decide?

Conclusion

3. How are protists different from bacteria? How are they alike?

____

____

____

Living things have requirements to live.

Prepare in Advance

Investigation 2: Obtain owl pellets. They may be ordered from a biological supply house or from companies specializing in owl pellets. (Look for these on the Internet.) If you wish, soak the pellets ahead of time.

Investigation 4: Obtain three small potted plants for each team. If you wish, grow them yourself or have students grow them as follows: Soak bean seeds overnight in water. Place a small amount of gravel in the bottom of each pot. Fill the pot with soil. Moisten the soil so that it is damp but not too wet. Add three to four bean seeds and cover with soil. Place the pots in a warm area out of direct light. Keep the soil moist. Once the plants are visible above the soil, place the pots in bright light.

Investigation 5: Soak radish seeds overnight in water.

Teacher Information

Living things all have basic requirements that must be met in order for them to stay alive. Most living things need air, water, food, and space to grow. Other factors that affect an organism's ability to survive include temperature and pressure.

All living things need food in one form or another. Food provides organisms with the energy they need to fuel their life processes. Some organisms, called **producers,** make their own food. Most producers convert the energy in sunlight to chemical energy (food) through the process of **photosynthesis.** Organisms that are not producers obtain food by consuming other living things. They are called **consumers.**

Air contains oxygen, carbon dioxide, and other gases. Most organisms need oxygen to live. The oxygen is used during the process of **respiration,** in which the energy in food is released and made available to the organism's cells. Green plants, algae, and some bacteria also need carbon dioxide. Carbon dioxide is one of the materials needed for photosynthesis.

Water is critical to life. The cells of most living things are about 70 percent water. Water is used, along with carbon dioxide, in the chemical reactions of photosynthesis. Some organisms, like cactuses, can survive for months or even years without taking in water. Others, like human beings, can survive for only a few days. Organisms that live in salt water also need fresh water. They have special adaptations that allow them to filter out the salt to get fresh water.

All organisms need a place to live. Some, like bacteria and protists, require only a small space. Others, like blue whales and hippopotamuses, need large amounts of space. Because space on Earth is limited, organisms often compete for what is available.

Concept 2 — Living Things

Four basic needs of all living things.

Food

Food provides fuel for energy.

Producers use the Sun's energy to produce their own food.

Some organisms get their food from producers.

Some animals get their food from other animals.

Air

Air contains oxygen, carbon dioxide, and other gases.

Plants need carbon dioxide to make food. Plants need oxygen to get energy from the food they make.

Mushrooms, bacteria, and protists need oxygen to get energy from food.

Animals need oxygen to get energy from the food they eat.

Water

Water is critical to life.

Plants take in water through their roots.

Amoebae take in water through their cell membrane.

People take in water by drinking.

Space

All organisms need a place to live.

A fish lives in ocean water.

Algae live on the surface of a pond.

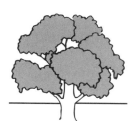

A tree grows in a field.

Living Things • EMC 881

Investigation 1

The Needs of Humans

Materials

- student record sheet on page 19, reproduced for each student
- sheets of paper

Steps to Follow

1. With the class, discuss the idea that living things need certain things in order to stay alive and healthy. Explain to students that they will begin to explore the requirements of life by keeping track of their own activities and needs. Invite them to speculate as to what they need to stay alive and healthy. Have them write their ideas on their record sheets.

2. Instruct students to copy the chart on the record sheet onto a sheet of paper. Have them use this chart to keep track of all their activities for a full 24-hour day. Discuss what they might include (washing, eating, walking to school, talking to friends, playing sports, doing homework, helping parents, etc.). Challenge them to include activities that they don't normally pay attention to (breathing, etc.).

3. After students collect their data, have them study it to determine what kinds of activities they engage in and how each benefits them. Discuss which activities are needed to keep them healthy and alive. Point out that activities like talking to friends and learning new things might not seem important, but help to keep people emotionally healthy.

4. Challenge students to use their conclusions to suggest what other kinds of animals need in order to stay healthy and alive. Help them to identify four basic needs of animals: food, water, air, and space.

Follow-Up

Show students the *Food Guide Pyramid*. Have them evaluate their diet. Discuss the effects of different eating habits on a person's health.

Invite a doctor or nurse to come to class to discuss the work they do in helping to keep people healthy.

Have teams of two students research how a particular kind of animal lives, what it needs to stay alive, and how it gets those things. Invite students to present their findings to the class either visually or orally.

The Needs of Humans

Procedure and Observations

1. What do you think you need to stay alive and healthy?

   _____

   _____

   _____

2. Copy the chart below onto a sheet of paper. Add more rows.

3. Keep track of all your activities for 24 hours. Tell what each activity gives you.

Time	Activity	What Does It Give Me?

Conclusions

4. What different kinds of activities do you do during the day?

   _____

   _____

5. Which of these give you something you need to live? What else do they give you?

   _____

   _____

6. What do you think other organisms need in order to stay healthy and alive?

   Plants: _____

   Animals: _____

   Fungi: _____

   Bacteria and Protists: _____

Investigation 2

Dissecting Owl Pellets

Materials

See advance preparation on page 16.

- student record sheet on page 21, reproduced for each student
- hand lenses
- owl pellets
- paper cups
- paper plates
- round toothpicks
- water

Steps to Follow

1. Invite students to suggest what they think owls eat. Explain that owls are hunters, and that they eat the animals they catch (their prey) whole. Tell students that owls then spit up any remains they cannot digest. Show students an owl pellet. Tell them that it contains the undigested part of one meal.

2. Tell students that they will dissect an owl pellet in order to determine what owls eat. Invite them to predict what they will find. Have them record their predictions on their record sheets.

3. Give each team an owl pellet on a paper plate. Have them place the pellet in a cup of water and let it soak for about 5 minutes.

4. Instruct students to use toothpicks to gently tease apart the pellet to see what they find. Tell them they must work slowly in order not to break anything.

5. Challenge students to group bones of similar structure. Suggest that they use a hand lens in order to see the bones more clearly. Then ask them to try to determine how many animals this owl had eaten.

6. Discuss with students what they have learned from this investigation about the needs of an owl. Challenge them to explain their answers.

Follow-Up

Explain to students that an owl produces anywhere from two to four pellets a day. Challenge students to calculate how many small animals an owl eats in a day, a week, a month, or a year.

Provide students with a bone-sorting chart that shows individual bones of different kinds of small animals. Challenge them to try to put together a complete skeleton and to determine what kind of animal it is. Have them sort the bones on a sheet of paper. Then have them glue the bones together to form a complete skeleton.

Dissecting Owl Pellets

Prediction

1. What do you think you will find inside your owl pellet?

_____

Procedure and Observations

2. Soak an owl pellet in water for 5 minutes.

3. Use toothpicks to dissect the pellet.

4. Sort what you find.

5. Draw and describe what you find in the owl pellet.

_____

_____

_____

6. How many animals do you think this owl ate?

_____

Conclusion

7. What did the owl pellet show about the needs of an owl?

_____

_____

Investigation 3

Meeting Animals' Needs

Materials

- student record sheet on page 23, reproduced for each student
- dice

Steps to Follow

1. Discuss the basic needs of animals (food, air, water, and space or shelter). Explain that all animals need these things to survive.

2. Invite a volunteer to explain what a model is. Make sure students understand that a model is something that represents something else. Tell the class that in this activity they will play a game to show, or model, what happens to a group of animals when their basic needs are either met or not met. Explain that this activity will deal only with food, water, and shelter.

3. Divide the class into groups of four. Have each student choose an animal that is native to your area and write it above the chart on their record sheets.

4. Review the directions for the game. Make sure students understand how to play. Give each group a die and have them play 10 rounds. Remind students to record the results of every round.

Sample Round

Round #	Numbers Rolled	Needs Met	Births or Deaths	Size of Population
1	1 4 6 1 5	food, water, shelter	1 birth	11

Follow-Up

Have students make a bar graph of their results. They should write the number of animals on the vertical axis and rounds on the horizontal axis.

Have the students simulate a drought by playing so that a 3 no longer has any value. Only a 4 can give the animals water. Have students compare the results of the first and second games. Discuss the differences. Invite students to suggest other factors that could affect the ability of the animals to stay alive.

Name _____

Meeting Animals' Needs

Procedure and Observations

1. Choose an animal. Write its name above the chart. Begin with a population of 10 animals.

2. Roll the die five times in a row. Record each roll in the first row of the "Numbers Rolled" column. A 1 or 2 gives your animals food, 3 or 4 gives them water, and 5 or 6 gives them shelter. If your animals get all three, 1 offspring is born. If your animals do not get all three, 1 member of the population dies. After each round, record the number of animals in your population.

3. After 10 rounds, compare the sizes of the animal populations in each round.

Type of Animal _____

Round #	Numbers Rolled	Needs Met	Births or Deaths	Size of Population
1				
2				
3				
4				
5				
6				
7				
8				
9				
10				

Conclusions

4. What happens to a group of animals if their needs are not met?

_____

5. What happens to a group of animals if their needs are met?

_____

Investigation 4

Plants, Water, and Light

Materials

See advance preparation on page 16.

- student record sheet on page 25, reproduced for each student
- small potted plants
- masking tape
- light source
- water

Steps to Follow

1. Review the basic needs of animals. Invite students to speculate as to the basic needs of plants. Tell them that in this activity they will investigate what happens to plants with and without light and water. Invite students' predictions.

2. Divide the class into teams. Give each team three small potted plants. Have them label the pots "Water & light," "Light no water," and "Water no light."

3. Tell students to water the plants labeled "Water & light." Instruct them to place these plants in a bright area and give these plants additional water whenever they begin to dry out.

4. Have students place the plants labeled "Light no water" in bright light. Instruct them not to give these plants any additional water.

5. Provide a dark place for students to put the plants labeled "Water no light." Instruct students to water these plants as needed.

6. After about 10 days, have students observe the plants. Tell them to record their observations on their record sheets.

Follow-Up

Have students continue to observe the plants for another week or two. Discuss any additional changes they notice. Ask them what they think will eventually happen to the plants without water or without light.

Challenge students to compare the effects of varying amounts of light on plants. Or, have them explore the amount of light needed by different kinds of plants. Help students design and carry out experiments to test these ideas.

Obtain a potted cactus. Have students observe how long the cactus can go without water before it begins to wilt.

Name _____

Plants, Water, and Light

Prediction

1. What do you think will happen to plants if they have either no water or no light?

   _____

Procedure and Observations

2. Put labels on three pots:
   Water & light
   Light no water
   Water no light

3. Prepare each pot according to its label. Place the "Water no light" pot in a dark place, and the other two pots in a well-lit place. Water the plants that should get water every few days.

4. After about 10 days, observe the plants.

5. Describe the appearance of each plant.

   Water & light: _____

   Light no water: _____

   Water no light: _____

Conclusions

6. What happens to a plant when it does not get any light?

   _____

7. What happens to a plant when it does not get any water?

   _____

8. What are two basic needs of plants?

   _____

Investigation 5

A Place to Live

Materials

See advance preparation on page 16.

- student record sheet on page 27, reproduced for each student
- gravel
- newspaper
- small plastic plant pots
- saucers for pots
- potting soil
- radish seeds
- water
- light source

Steps to Follow

1. Have students spread newspaper over their work area. Provide each team with two small plastic pots and saucers, potting soil, and gravel. Have them place a small amount of gravel in the bottom of each pot and fill the pot with soil. Tell them to add water to moisten the soil. Have them make sure the soil is moist but not too wet.

2. Instruct students to place 4 to 6 radish seeds in one pot and 30 to 40 radish seeds in the second pot. Have them cover the seeds with a thin layer of soil. Provide a warm area out of direct sunlight where students can put the pots.

3. Once the plants are visible above the soil, have students place the pots under a lamp or in direct sunlight. Each day or two, have them turn the pots one-quarter turn. Remind students to keep the soil moist but not soaking wet.

4. Ask students what basic needs they are providing for the radish plants.

5. When the plants in the pot with a few seeds are about 1 to 2" (2.5 to 5 cm) tall (after about 7 to 8 days), tell students to pull out all but the two healthiest seedlings.

6. Have students observe the plants in both pots every 4 to 5 days for about 2 to 3 weeks. Tell them to record their observations on their record sheets.

Follow-Up

Review all the needs of plants that students have investigated (water, light, and space).

A Place to Live

Procedure and Observations

1. Place gravel in the bottom of two pots. Fill the pots with soil. Moisten the soil.

2. In one pot, plant 4 to 6 radish seeds. In the second pot, plant 30 to 40 radish seeds.

3. When the seeds sprout, place the pots in bright light. Make regular observations of the radish plants. Record them on the chart.

Date	Pot with Two Plants	Pot with Many Plants

Conclusions

4. In which pot do the radish plants look healthier? How do they look better?

_____

5. How does the amount of space available affect the growth of plants?

_____

3

Living things reproduce.

Prepare in Advance

Investigation 1: Purchase large complete flowers (those with both stamens and pistils) such as gladiolus or lilies. You may also use roses with only a single set of petals, but beware of the thorns.

Investigation 3: Purchase a potato for each team of students.

Investigation 4: Purchase regular button mushrooms from the grocery store. Look for ones with large flat caps, dark gills, and complete stalks. You might want to purchase a few other varieties for discussion.

Investigation 5: Obtain mealworms from a bait-supply store or pet store, or order them from a biological supply house. Collect plastic yogurt containers with lids, or other small containers, and punch several small holes in each lid.

Teacher Information

Flowering plants reproduce through **sexual reproduction,** which requires a male and a female contribution. A flower has an outer layer of **sepals** and an inner layer of **petals** that may attract insects. **Pollen grains** form on the tip of the **stamen,** the male reproductive organ. Inside each pollen grain is a sperm cell. The bottom of the **pistil,** the female reproductive organ, is enlarged and is the site of **ovule,** or egg cell, formation. When a pollen grain lands on the tip of a pistil, a tube grows out of the pollen grain and down the pistil. The sperm cell moves down this tube to the egg cell. The two cells join together and develop into a seed, which is encased in a fruit.

Many plants also reproduce through **asexual reproduction,** which is also known as **vegetative reproduction** because it involves growth of vegetative parts.

Most mushrooms and other fungi reproduce by **spores.** Microscopic spores are produced in the gills, located on the underside of the mushroom cap. Spores are dispersed by wind. When they encounter favorable conditions, they begin to grow, and long, branched, hair-like hyphae form. A web-like mass, the mycelium, develops from the hyphae. The mushroom stalks, which are the reproductive organs, grow up out of the mycelium. Each produces millions of tiny spores that are so small that they can be seen only with a powerful microscope.

Mealworms are the **larvae** of the darkling beetle. These beetles undergo **complete metamorphosis.** The female beetles lay about 500 to 1,000 tiny bean-shaped white eggs. After about a week, the eggs hatch into tiny larvae. The larvae eat constantly and grow rapidly. As the larvae grow, they molt, or shed their exoskeletons, several times. After several months, the larvae spin an outer covering and form **pupae.** The pupae undergo rapid changes, and after about two weeks adult beetles emerge.

Complete metamorphosis involves four distinct stages: egg, larva, pupa, and adult. Some animals, such as frogs and grasshoppers, undergo incomplete metamorphosis, which involves only three stages—egg, nymph, and adult.

Life Cycles

Flowering Plant

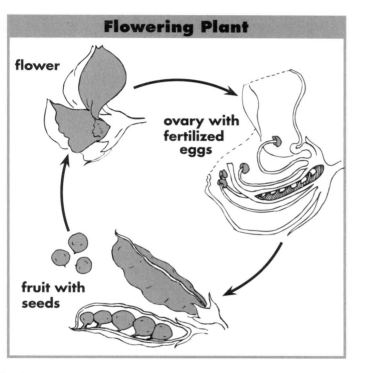

flower

ovary with fertilized eggs

fruit with seeds

Mushroom

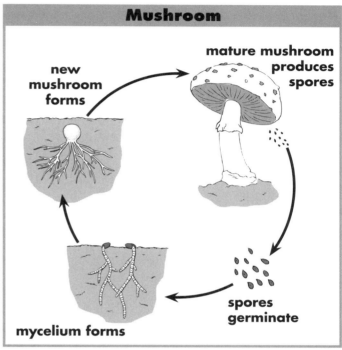

new mushroom forms

mature mushroom produces spores

spores germinate

mycelium forms

Butterfly

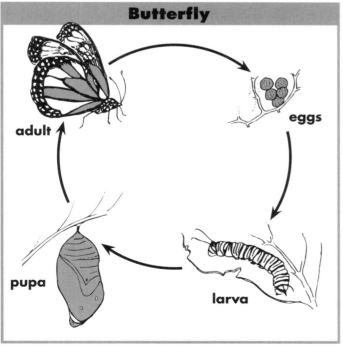

adult

eggs

pupa

larva

Grasshopper

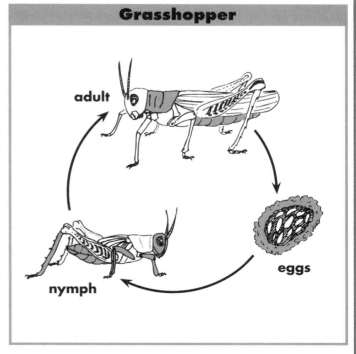

adult

eggs

nymph

Investigation 1

Looking at Flowers

Materials

See advance preparation on page 28.

- student record sheet on page 31, reproduced for each student
- large flowers, such as gladiolus, lilies, or roses
- hand lenses
- paper clips
- transparent tape
- white paper

Steps to Follow

1. Write the word **reproduce** on the board. Invite students to suggest what it means. Explain that all living things reproduce, and without reproduction, a species would die out.

2. Show students a flower. Explain that many plants reproduce using flowers. Point out the diagram on the record sheet. Review the names of the flower parts and the function of each. Explain that seeds form in the flowers, and then the seeds grow into new plants. In this way, flowering plants reproduce.

3. Give each team a flower and a hand lens. Have them set the flower on a sheet of paper. Challenge them to find the petals, sepals, pistil, and stamens.

4. Show students how to straighten out one end of a paper clip and use it to cut down the center of the flower. After students cut open their flowers, have them draw the inside view of the flower on their record sheets and label the parts.

5. Tell students to separate the parts of the flower. Caution them not to break anything. Have them place the petals and sepals on the paper, tape them in place, and label them.

6. Have students observe the stamens. Tell them to touch the knob to the paper. Ask them to identify what falls off. Have students place the stamens and some pollen on the paper, tape them down, and label them. Explain the function of stamens.

7. Challenge students to find the pistil and to notice its enlarged bottom. Discuss what is found in the base of the pistil and what forms there. Have students cut open the pistil and observe the inside. Have them tape the pistil to the paper.

Follow-Up

Discuss how pollen is transferred from the stamens of one flower or plant to the pistil of another and how seeds form. Emphasize the important role that insects, mammals, and birds play in the reproduction of flowering plants.

Provide a variety of flowers. Discuss how the sepals, petals, pistils, and stamens compare in each flower. Challenge students to explain any differences.

Looking at Flowers

Procedure and Observations

1. Study the parts of a flower.

2. Observe a flower. Count the petals and sepals. Find the pistil and stamens. Use a hand lens for all your observations.

3. Open a paper clip. Cut open the flower.

4. Draw the inside of the flower. Label the parts.

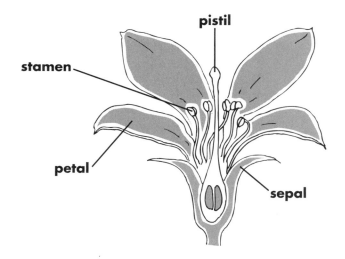

Conclusion

5. How does a flower function in plant reproduction? Use the names of all the flower parts in your answer.

_____

_____

_____

Investigation 2

Traveling Seeds

Materials

- student record sheet on page 33, reproduced for each student
- old socks
- white paper
- hand lenses
- transparent tape

Steps to Follow

1. Have students slip an old sock, turned inside out, over one hand or one shoe. Take them for a walk in a vacant lot or open field in the fall when the weather has been fairly dry.

2. Instruct students to drag the sock along the ground and brush it up against as many plants as they can. Tell them to try especially to touch any burrs or similar structures, whether on the ground or at head height.

3. After 10 to 15 minutes, have students remove their sock, turning it right-side out again in the process. Encourage them to save everything that has collected on the sock.

4. Back inside, have students remove everything that attached to the sock and place it on a sheet of white paper. Discuss what these things are (seeds, or fruits containing seeds).

5. Provide students with hand lenses to examine the seeds. Challenge them to group them by their similarities. Tell them to sketch on their record sheets what they see through the hand lens.

6. Encourage students to mount a sample of each seed on a sheet of paper. Beneath it, have them describe how they think the seed is dispersed.

7. Discuss the structure of the seeds with the students and how the structure relates to the dispersal of the seeds. Be sure they notice structures such as burrs that allow the seeds to stick to a passerby. Encourage students to suggest additional ways that seeds are transported naturally (through the dung of animals that feed on them; by floating on the wind or water).

8. Discuss the importance of seed dispersal to plant survival. Invite students to describe what would happen if all the seeds landed right under the parent plant.

Follow-Up

Explain that the Velcro® fastener was invented in 1951 by a Swiss man, George de Mestral, who had observed burrs clinging to his pants. Have students research the physical structure of Velcro® (www.velcro.com).

Have students plant several of each kind of seed in potting soil. Invite students to sketch the plants at various stages of their development. Provide plant identification guides and challenge students to identify what they see growing.

Name _____

Traveling Seeds

Procedure and Observations

1. Put an old sock over your hand or shoe. Brush it against as many plants as you can.

2. Remove everything that stuck to the sock. Put it on a sheet of white paper.

3. Sort the seeds by their appearance. Look at them with a hand lens. Draw what you see below.

4. Tape the seeds to a sheet of paper. Describe how each one travels.

Conclusions

5. How do the seeds you collected move around?

_____

6. What are some other ways that seeds travel?

_____

7. Why is it important for seeds to move away from the plant where they formed?

_____

_____

Investigation 3

Vegetative Reproduction

Materials

See advance preparation on page 28.

- student record sheet on page 35, reproduced for each student
- jars
- potatoes
- toothpicks
- water

Steps to Follow

1. Show the class a potato. Explain that a potato is a tuber, or a swollen underground stem. Point out the buds, or "eyes."

2. Give each team a potato with "eyes." Ask them to predict what will happen if they put it in water. Have them record their predictions on their record sheets.

3. Provide students with toothpicks and jars. Tell them to set up their potato in water as shown in the illustration on the record sheet.

4. Have students make and record regular observations of their potatoes. Discuss what happens.

5. Challenge students to explain the importance of their observations in terms of potato reproduction. Explain that the method they used to grow new potato plants is an example of **vegetative reproduction** because the plant reproduced from its vegetative parts, not from its flowers. Explain that potato plants also reproduce through flowers like other flowering plants.

Follow-Up

Allow students to let their potatoes continue to grow. Once roots have formed, provide pots and potting soil for them to plant the potatoes.

Tell students that farmers cut up potatoes into pieces, each containing an "eye," or new bud. They then plant these pieces to make more potato plants. Discuss how many plants they can get from each potato.

Invite students to try to get other plants to reproduce by vegetative reproduction. Challenge them to try root and stem cuttings. Provide them with fresh horseradish leaves or philodendron leaves.

Vegetative Reproduction

Prediction

1. What do you think will happen to a potato that is put in water?

_____

Procedure and Observations

2. Stick four toothpicks into the potato.

3. Fill a jar almost to the top with water.

4. Place the potato in the jar of water.

5. Observe the potato every few days.
   Record your observations.

Date	Observation of Potato

Conclusions

6. What changes did you observe in the potato?

_____

_____

7. How is a potato "eye" like a seed? How is it different?

_____

_____

_____

Investigation 4

Multiplying Mushrooms

Materials

See advance preparation on page 28.

- student record sheet on page 37, reproduced for each student
- mushrooms
- hand lenses
- bowls, larger than the mushrooms
- plastic knives
- white paper

Steps to Follow

1. Review the various kingdoms. Explain to students that members of the Kingdom Fungi reproduce differently than do plants. Review the characteristics of mushrooms.

2. Give each group a mushroom and a hand lens. Using the diagram on the record sheet, have students identify the parts of the mushroom. Challenge them to hypothesize how mushrooms reproduce. Have them record their ideas on their record sheets.

3. Instruct students to gently pull off the stalk of the mushroom from the cap. If the outer rim of the cap curves down to hide the gills on the underside, have students carefully trim it away.

4. Tell students to lay the mushroom cap gill-side down on the paper. Have them cover it with a bowl and leave it overnight.

5. The next day, tell students to carefully lift the bowl and the mushroom cap from the paper. Discuss what they observe. Explain that the design on the paper was made by **spores,** the reproductive parts of fungi, which were released from the gills in the mushroom cap.

6. Invite volunteers to compare mushroom spores with the seeds they observed previously.

Follow-Up

Provide students with pictures of a variety of kinds of fungi. Have them locate the spore-producing parts.

If students wish to keep their designs, you may spray the spore prints with hair spray to preserve them.

Name _____

Multiplying Mushrooms

Prediction

1. How do you think mushrooms reproduce?

_____

Procedure and Observations

2. Identify the parts of the mushroom.

3. Place the cap gill-side down on a sheet of paper. Cover it with a bowl. Leave it overnight.

4. Take the mushroom cap off the paper. Observe the paper.

5. What do you observe on the paper after you take off the mushroom?

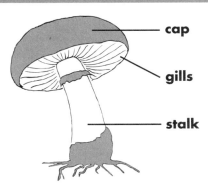

cap

gills

stalk

_____

_____

_____

6. What causes this?

_____

_____

_____

Conclusions

7. How do mushrooms reproduce?

_____

8. What is similar about how plants and fungi reproduce? What is different?

_____

_____

Concept

3

Living Things

Investigation 5

Insect Metamorphosis

Materials

See advance preparation on page 28.

- student record sheet on page 39, reproduced for each student
- yogurt containers, with lids with holes punched
- wheat bran
- marking pens
- masking tape
- mealworms
- hand lenses
- potato, cut into small pieces

Steps to Follow

1. Show students the mealworms. Ask what they must give the mealworms in order for them to grow and reproduce (air, water, food, and space). Ask students to predict what kinds of changes they will observe in the mealworms. Have them record their predictions on their record sheets.

2. Give each team a yogurt container and have them fill it about ¼ full with wheat bran. Instruct them to label the container with their name and the date.

3. Have each team put 3 to 4 mealworms in their container and add a small piece of potato. Provide a dark area where students can put their containers.

4. Have students check their mealworms every few days and record any changes they see. Tell them to observe and record the mealworms' behavior. Make sure students regularly replace the old potato, as rot will kill the mealworms. After about six weeks, have students add more bran to their containers.

5. Invite students to describe what they have observed.

6. Discuss the reproduction and life stages of a mealworm. Explain to students that the mealworms have undergone **metamorphosis** and changed into beetles. Tell them that the beetles will mate and lay eggs that are too small to be seen.

Stages of Mealworm Life Cycle

larva   **pupa**   **adult**

Follow-Up

Once beetles have formed, you may wish to have students continue to observe the changes until new larvae form.

Discuss other animals that undergo metamorphosis during their life stages. Invite students to research different animals and make posters to show their life stages.

Insect Metamorphosis

Prediction

1. How do you think your mealworms will change over the next several weeks?

_____

Procedure and Observations

2. Label the container with your team members' names. Fill it about ¼ full with wheat bran. Add a piece of potato and three to four mealworms. Place the lid tightly on the container.

3. Make regular observations of the mealworms. Watch how they behave. Record what you see. Include drawings to show how the animals look. Use the back of this sheet for your drawings.

Date	Observations	
	Physical Appearance	**Behavior**

Conclusion

4. How do mealworms grow, change, and reproduce?

_____

_____

_____

_____

4

Ecosystems are made up of living things and nonliving factors.

Prepare in Advance

Investigation 2: Identify and inspect an outdoor location such as an empty lot, a wooded area, a meadow, the schoolyard, or a park where students can do an ecosystem study. If you plan to take the students off school property, make sure you follow any school regulations concerning such activities.

Investigation 3: Obtain small plants that are suitable for a terrarium. You may purchase these from a nursery or garden center, or collect them yourself from an area where this is allowed. Collect earthworms by digging in humus-rich soil, or purchase them from a bait shop or an aquarium-supply store.

Investigation 4: Allow tap water to sit overnight to make it safe for fish and snails. Purchase cold-water guppies, pond snails, freshwater algae, and plants such as elodea and duckweed at a pet shop or an aquarium-supply store. If you wish to collect aquatic organisms yourself, find a pond, wetland, or quiet stream where collection is not prohibited. Sweep a fish net through an area thick with water plants to collect both plants and snails. Fill a plastic jar halfway with water, add the plants and snails, and cover. Prepare a paper cup for each team with a small amount of algae, a few plants, three to four snails, and two to three guppies in pond water or water that has stood overnight.

Investigation 5: Prepare ice cubes. Put liquid food coloring in the refrigerator to chill.

Teacher Information

A group of organisms living together that are all the same **species** makes up a **population**. A **community** is all the different populations that live in a certain area at a certain time. An **ecosystem** is made up of the community of living things along with all the nonliving factors that affect the community. For example, a forest ecosystem includes all the trees, shrubs, and small plants; all the fungi; all the protists and bacteria; and all the animals, such as squirrels and deer, that live in the forest. The forest ecosystem also includes nonliving factors, such as soil, rocks, water, light, and temperature, that affect the living things.

The Earth contains a wide variety of ecosystems. The kinds of organisms that live in an ecosystem are in large part determined by the nonliving factors. Cactuses and other succulents grow in a desert, where there is very little water. On high mountaintops, it is very windy, and temperatures are extreme. Only organisms that can survive in such conditions grow there. Along the rocky seashore, tides rise and fall. Barnacles, sea anemones, and other organisms have structures or adaptations that allow them to live in this ever-changing environment.

A Pond Ecosystem

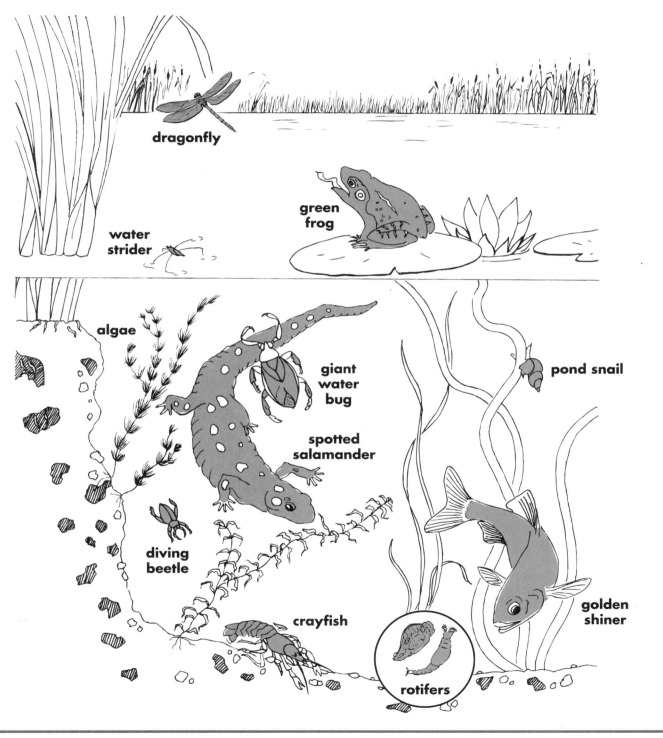

dragonfly

water
strider

green
frog

algae

giant
water
bug

spotted
salamander

pond snail

diving
beetle

crayfish

rotifers

golden
shiner

Concept 4

Living Things

Investigation 1

What's in an Ecosystem?

Materials

- student record sheet on page 43, reproduced for each student
- resource and reference books on world ecosystems
- posterboard
- markers and other art supplies for making posters

Steps to Follow

1. Write the term **ecosystem** on the board. Explain to students that an ecosystem is all of the living things and all of the nonliving factors that interact in a specific area. Invite students to identify some ecosystems in their area (for example, a pond, empty lot, or park). Tell them that an ecosystem can be as large as the ocean or as small as a puddle. Ask them to identify a few factors that might be found in one or more of these ecosystems.

2. Divide the class into small groups. Challenge students to brainstorm a list of as many factors as they can think of that might be found in an ecosystem. When they finish, make a class list of all their factors.

3. Invite the class to brainstorm a list of different kinds of ecosystems. Have them begin with ones they may be familiar with, but then challenge them to think of other ecosystems they have seen in books and movies, and on television.

4. Assign one major ecosystem to each group. Instruct them to use the class list of ecosystem factors to identify those factors that would be found in their ecosystem (for example, ocean ecosystem: water, light, plants, animals, etc.).

5. Have each team research their ecosystem to find out more about the living and nonliving factors in it. Encourage them to learn about specific organisms and details about nonliving factors, such as rainfall and temperature. Have each team make a poster or other visual display of the factors present in their ecosystem.

Follow-Up

Invite teams to make oral presentations to the class. Discuss differences and similarities among world ecosystems.

Discuss what kinds of ecosystems humans live in and how people affect the ecosystems around them. Challenge students to create their ideal ecosystem. Encourage them to include a variety of living and nonliving factors in their description. Ask them to explain why they would like living in this ecosystem.

What's in an Ecosystem?

Procedure and Observations

1. What living and nonliving factors can be found in an ecosystem?

━━━━━━━━━━━━━━ Living Factors ━━━━━━━━━━━━━━

_____

_____

_____

━━━━━━━━━━━━ Nonliving Factors ━━━━━━━━━━━━

_____

_____

_____

2. Help make a class list of factors that can be found in ecosystems.

3. With the class, brainstorm a list of ecosystems.

4. Choose one ecosystem. What factors from the class list can be found in that ecosystem? Read about your ecosystem. Identify other factors found in it.

5. Make a poster to show the living and nonliving factors in your ecosystem. Share it with your classmates.

Conclusion

6. How is the ecosystem you studied similar to other ecosystems? How is it different?

_____

_____

_____

_____

Investigation 2

Exploring an Ecosystem

Materials

See advance preparation on page 40.

- student record sheets on pages 46–48, reproduced for each student
- string
- compasses
- metersticks
- thermometers
- craft sticks
- trowels
- reclosable plastic bags
- index cards
- masking tape
- hand lenses
- chart paper

Steps to Follow

1. Tell students they will now observe a real ecosystem. Review the procedures, including the instructions on the record sheet, and provide the materials. Tell students where they will do their study. Invite them to predict what they will find. Have them write their ideas on their record sheets.

2. Before heading out to the study site, review safety procedures with the class. **Students should not handle any mushrooms whatsoever as some species are poisonous.** They should be aware of stinging insects. They should not collect any samples without your permission. Once back in the classroom, they should wash their hands immediately with warm water and soap.

3. Outdoors, assign each team of two to one section of the ecosystem. Have them use the string as a compass and mark off a circle 2 meters in diameter. Tell them to identify the boundary of their area with stones, leaves, or twigs. Have them sketch the area on the record sheet.

4. Have teams observe and record air temperature, relative wind speed, moisture content of soil, and degree of soil compaction in their area. Have them collect a soil sample and identify nonliving factors in their area, including those added by people, such as sidewalks. Remind them to accurately record all observations.

5. Have students observe the trees, bushes, and other plants in their area, as well as mushrooms or other fungi. Encourage them to use their hand lens. If allowed, have them collect sample leaves in separate reclosable bags. Tell them to describe and sketch each kind of organism on a separate index card and to number the cards to correlate to any samples.

6. Have students look for signs of animal life, such as tracks or evidence of animals having eaten. Instruct them to collect any animal remains such as fur, feathers, or human litter in separate reclosable bags. Encourage students to watch for birds and other small animals, such as ants and squirrels. Instruct them to record their observations of animals as they did with the plants and fungi.

7. Back in the classroom, have students continue their observations by using a hand lens to search for living things in the soil. Tell them to write their observations and sketch the animals on separate index cards.

8. Instruct teams to transfer their observations to a large sheet of chart paper and tape their index cards and samples on the paper. Tell them to put each sample next to the corresponding card.

9. Have teams present their data to the class. Ask the class to compare and contrast the results from the various groups.

Follow-Up

Display the students' data sheets around the classroom. Provide time for students to carefully study each other's observations. Create a classroom chart that summarizes the findings of the class. Discuss how all the data together helps create an understanding of the entire ecosystem.

Have students create a class map or diorama of the ecosystem they observed.

Repeat the activity with the class at different seasons of the year. Use the same areas. Have students compare and contrast their data charts for individual areas and for the whole area. Discuss the seasonal changes in this ecosystem.

Name _____

Exploring an Ecosystem

Prediction

1. What living and nonliving factors do you think make up a nearby ecosystem?

_____

Procedure and Observations

2. Mark off an area 2 meters in diameter using the string as a compass.

3. Make a sketch of the area below. Use your compass to find North, South, East, and West. Mark these on your drawing.

4. Make and record observations of your area on separate index cards and on the following two record sheets.

5. Display your findings. Compare your findings with those of your classmates.

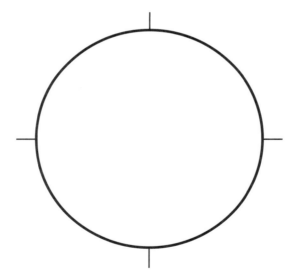

Conclusions

6. How is your area like those of your classmates? How is it different?

_____

_____

7. On the back of this sheet, write a description of the ecosystem your class studied.

Exploring an Ecosystem continued

Procedure and Observations—Nonliving Factors

8. Look for nonliving factors such as water, stones, and sidewalks. List them.

_____

_____

Temperature:

9. Hold the thermometer at shoulder height. Do not touch the bulb. Wait about a minute. Read and record the temperature.

10. Lay the thermometer on the ground. Wait one minute. Read and record the temperature.

11. With a trowel, dig 7 cm into the ground. Measure and record the temperature.

Location	Temp (°F)
Air	
Ground	
Underground	

Wind Speed:

12. Look at the trees and bushes. Use the following scale to decide how hard the wind is blowing. Check the correct line.

- ☐ *No wind*–trees and bushes are not moving
- ☐ *Breezy*–trees and bushes are moving slightly
- ☐ *Windy*–trees and bushes are moving quite a bit
- ☐ *Very windy*–trees and bushes are swaying hard

Soil

13. Push a craft stick into the soil. How easily does it go in?

- ☐ *Very soft*–like pushing into soft ice cream
- ☐ *Soft*–like pushing into a snowball or banana
- ☐ *Hard*–like pushing into clay
- ☐ *Very hard*–stick almost breaks or cannot be pushed in

14. Dig up a small amount of soil with the trowel. Hold it in your hand. Feel it and record how it feels.

15. Put a small amount of soil in a plastic bag. Seal the bag. Take it inside to search for living things.

- ☐ *Dry*–soil falls apart and sifts through your fingers
- ☐ *Slightly moist*–soil looks moist but does not stick together when squeezed
- ☐ *Moist*–soil clumps together when squeezed
- ☐ *Very moist*–soil feels wet when squeezed
- ☐ *Wet*–water drips out of soil when squeezed

Procedure and Observations—Living Factors

Plant and Fungus Life:

16. How many different kinds of plants can you find? Look for trees, bushes, and small plants. For each one, use a separate index card to record your observations. Describe and draw the plant.

17. If it is allowed, collect a leaf of each plant. Put each leaf in a separate plastic bag and seal it. Using masking tape, label the bag with a number. Write the same number on the index card where you described the plant.

18. Look for fungi, but *do not touch any fungi.* Look on the ground and on dead or living trees. For each kind you find, make a separate index card. Draw and describe the fungus.

Animal Life:

19. Collect remains of animals such as fur, feathers, and human litter. Put each piece in a separate plastic bag. To collect the remains without touching them, turn the bag inside out. Then put your hand in the bag, pick up the material, and pull the top of the bag around the material. Seal the bag.

20. On separate index cards, describe and sketch signs of animals that cannot be collected, such as burrows, nests, and footprints.

21. Look for animals on the ground and in trees. On separate index cards, describe and sketch any animals you actually see. Note and record each animal's behavior.

22. In the classroom, look at the soil. Use a hand lens. For each organism you find, make a card. Sketch and describe the organism. Note and record its behavior.

Concept 4 Living Things

Investigation 3
A Land Ecosystem

Materials

See advance preparation on page 40.

- student record sheet on page 50, reproduced for each student
- earthworms
- gravel
- large spoons
- newspapers
- plastic wrap
- potting soil
- large rubber bands
- small plants
- water
- large wide-mouth jars

Steps to Follow

1. Discuss what a terrarium is. Invite students to explain how it is a miniature ecosystem. Tell students they will make terrariums and observe them over time.

2. Provide each team with the materials. Have them spread newspapers over their workspace. Instruct them to cover the bottom of the jar with gravel. Then have students add a thick layer of soil.

3. Demonstrate how to add plants to the terrarium. With a large spoon, dig a small hole in the soil. Put the plant in the hole, cover the roots with soil, and press down the soil around the plant. Have students add several plants to their jar.

4. Provide students with earthworms to add to their mini-ecosystems.

5. Have students sprinkle the soil with water and cover their terrarium with plastic wrap. Instruct them to punch a few air holes in the plastic. Have them secure the plastic with a rubber band. Remind students to wash their hands after handling animals or soil that has not been sterilized.

6. Ask students to name the living and nonliving factors present in their terrarium. Have them record their answers on their record sheets. Provide an area for the terrariums that is warm and well lit, but out of direct sunlight.

7. Have students check their terrariums daily for 2 to 3 days to make sure they have enough water, but not too much. If water condenses on the inside of the jar, have them remove the plastic for a few hours and then replace it.

8. Have students observe their terrariums every few days for about three weeks. Encourage them to watch for changes and for interactions among organisms, and between living and nonliving things. Have them record their observations.

Follow-Up

Discuss how the needs of individual organisms are being met. Ask students how the various organisms interact. Invite them to speculate what will happen to each organism over time. Encourage students to keep their terrariums and to continue to make observations.

Provide sand and small cactuses from a nursery or garden center. Have students create desert terrariums. Discuss how desert ecosystems are similar to and different from other ecosystems.

A Land Ecosystem

Procedure and Observations

1. Cover the bottom of the jar with gravel. Add soil, plants, earthworms, and water to your terrarium.

2. Cover your terrarium with plastic wrap.

3. Set the terrarium in a warm place out of direct sunlight. Observe it regularly.

4. What living and nonliving factors are found in your mini-ecosystem?

_____

_____

5. Record your observations of the terrarium on the chart.

Date	Observations of Living and Nonliving Factors

Conclusion

6. Compare this ecosystem to the one you observed outside. How is it similar? How is it different?

_____

_____

Investigation 4

An Aquatic Ecosystem

Materials

See advance preparation on page 40.

- student record sheet on page 52, reproduced for each student
- newspapers
- aquarium gravel
- wooden dowel
- fish food
- fish net
- freshwater algae
- freshwater plants
- freshwater snails
- guppies
- hand lenses
- large wide-mouth jar or aquarium tank
- paper cups
- thermometers
- water

Steps to Follow

1. Explain to students that in this activity they will make and observe an aquatic ecosystem. Provide each team with the materials. Have them spread newspapers over their worktable. Tell them to spread a thin layer of gravel on the bottom of the jar. Provide water that has sat for 24 hours. Instruct students to fill their aquariums about ⅔ full of water.

2. Demonstrate how to add freshwater plants. Use a dowel to push rooted plants firmly into the gravel at the bottom of the tank. Place floating plants on the water's surface. Allow time for students to add plants to their aquariums.

3. Have students put their aquariums in a cool, bright area out of direct light or heat.

4. Have students check the water temperature with a thermometer to make sure it is between 18° and 26°C (68° to 78°F), the temperature needed by guppies. If necessary, help students adjust the water temperature by moving the aquariums to a warmer or cooler place.

5. Give each team a cup containing guppies and snails. Have them add the animals to their aquarium. Remind students not to touch the fish, as they could hurt the fish. Have them sprinkle a small amount of fish food on the water. Tell students to give the fish only as much as they can eat in 3 to 5 minutes. Explain that if they overfeed, the food will decay and foul the water.

6. Ask students what living and nonliving things make up this ecosystem.

7. Have students observe their aquariums and write their observations on their record sheets. Every few days have them make new observations and feed the fish. Encourage them to watch for interactions among living things, and between living and nonliving things.

Follow-Up

Discuss how this ecosystem is different from the terrarium ecosystem. Invite students to explain how the nonliving factors of an ecosystem affect the kinds of organisms that live there.

Have students investigate more about pond ecosystems. Encourage them to find out what other plants and animals live there and how they interact. Discuss the nonliving factors that make up a pond ecosystem. Challenge students to compare their aquarium to a real pond.

An Aquatic Ecosystem

Procedure and Observations

1. Put a layer of gravel in the bottom of a large jar. Fill the jar ⅔ full with water.

2. Add algae and plants.

3. Use a thermometer to check the water temperature. It should be between 18° and 26°C (68° to 78°F).

4. Add fish and snails. Feed the fish.

5. Observe the aquarium every few days.

6. What living and nonliving factors are found in your aquarium?

   _____

   _____

7. Record your observations of the aquarium on the chart.

Date	Observations of Living and Nonliving Factors

Conclusion

8. Compare this ecosystem to the one in the terrarium. How is it similar? How is it different? How can you explain these differences?

   _____

   _____

Investigation 5

A Nonliving Factor

Materials

See advance preparation on page 40.

- student record sheets on pages 54 and 55, reproduced for each student
- cold water
- clear plastic cups
- ice cubes
- food coloring
- hot water
- shallow container

Steps to Follow

1. Invite students to name some organisms that live in a pond or lake. Suggest that they begin with the organisms they put into their aquariums. Write their ideas on the board.

2. Ask students what they think happens to these organisms if the water in the lake freezes in winter. Encourage them to respond for a variety of different organisms. Tell students they will do experiments to show how a nonliving factor—water—reacts when it freezes and how that affects living things.

3. Have students fill a cup half full with water, add an ice cube, and notice what happens to the ice cube. (It floats.) Challenge them to speculate on how this fact affects the animals living in a pond or lake.

4. Have students fill two clear plastic cups with cold water and let the cups sit for about a minute. Have students fill the shallow container with about 1 inch (2.5 cm) of hot water. Tell them to place one drop of food coloring in each cup and immediately put one cup into the container of hot water. Warn them to jiggle the water as little as possible. Tell them to observe what happens to the food coloring in each cup. (The food coloring in the warm water bath circulates around the cup.) Suggest that they view the cups from the side in order to see more clearly. Remind them to record their observations on their record sheets.

5. Challenge students to speculate on how the behavior of cold water as it warms might affect pond or lake animals.

Follow-Up

Point out to students that many nutrients needed by aquatic organisms sink to the bottom of a pond or lake. Discuss the importance of the mixing of water and nutrients. Invite students to speculate at what times of year this is most likely to happen. Ask them to explain their answers.

A Nonliving Factor

Prediction

1. How do you think ice will behave in water?

   _____

Procedure and Observations

2. Fill a cup half full with water.

3. Add an ice cube. Observe what happens to the ice cube. Record your observations.

4. What happens to the ice cube when you put it in water? Where in the cup did it go?

   _____

   _____

   _____

   _____

   _____

   _____

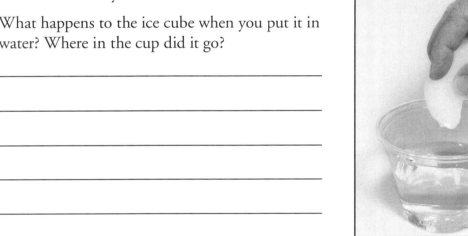

Conclusion

5. How might the behavior of ice in water affect organisms that live in ponds and lakes where the water freezes?

   _____

   _____

   _____

Prediction

6. How do you think warming will affect cold water?

_____

Procedure and Observations

7. Fill two cups with cold water. Let them sit.

8. Add hot water to a shallow container.

9. Add one drop of food coloring to each cup. Immediately place one cup in the shallow container of hot water.

10. Observe the food coloring in both cups for several minutes. Record your observations.

11. What happens to the food coloring in the two cups?

Not in hot water:

_____

In hot water:

_____

Conclusions

12. What happens to the water in a lake as it warms up in spring?

_____

_____

13. How might the behavior of cold water when it is heated affect organisms that live in ponds and lakes?

_____

_____

_____

Structures and behaviors of living things help them to survive in specific habitats.

Prepare in Advance

Investigation 1: Using a hole punch, punch colored acetate dots from report covers. Use at least five colors (more if groups of students need to be larger than five), and make about 30 dots of each color for each group. When students are not looking, spread a full sheet of multicolored wrapping paper on a flat surface for each group. Dump about 150 dots—an equal number of each color—onto each sheet and spread them around.

Investigation 3: Prepare large quantities of ice cubes.

Investigation 4: Obtain earthworms from an aquarium-supply store, a pet shop, a bait shop, or dig them up yourself. Put the worms in a container half full of moist soil. Add fresh leaves. Cover with cheesecloth secured with a rubber band. Keep worms in a cool place.

Investigation 5: Soak pinto beans in water overnight.

Teacher Information

Each kind of organism lives in a **habitat** that provides food, water, shelter, space, and air if needed. An organism's **adaptations** are structures and behaviors that help it to survive in its habitat.

Some prey animals use **camouflage** to prevent predators from finding them. The walking stick is an insect that looks like a stick. At rest on the branch of a tree, it blends in and cannot easily be seen. Camouflage may take the form of protective coloration. Some grasshoppers are almost the same color as leaves.

An important physical adaptation in humans and apes is the **opposable thumb.** Chimpanzees use their thumbs to remove parasites from each other. They hold sticks and probe for termites. Humans use thumbs to hold many different things.

Many animals live in very cold or hot places. Some fish in Antarctica have an antifreeze-like compound in their blood to keep it from freezing. Whales, seals, and other animals have a thick layer of fat known as blubber. Blubber provides insulation and helps keep these mammals warm in the cold ocean waters.

Earthworms tunnel through the soil, eating plant matter and depositing their wastes as they go. They have behavioral adaptations to help them survive. They move toward moist areas, which helps to keep them from drying out and dying. They move away from light, which keeps them from crawling about on the surface of the ground, where they would be exposed to the drying air.

Plants have behavioral adaptations known as **tropisms.** Plant roots respond to gravity by growing downward. This helps them find soil and water. Plant stems grow upward, where they are most likely to find light.

Some Adaptations of Plants and Animals

The katydid is covered with sharp spikes that make it look dangerous and help protect it from predators.

When white-tailed deer run away from danger, they raise their white tails, which serves as a signal to other deer.

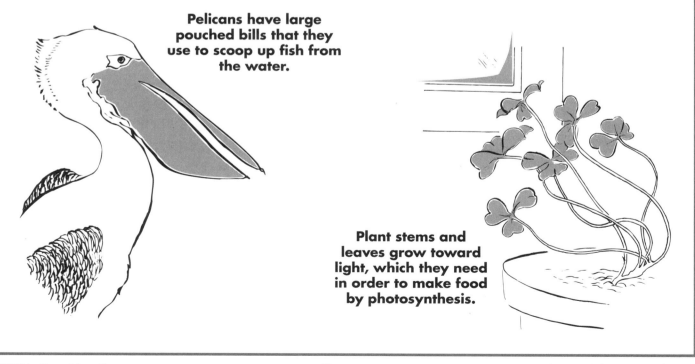

Pelicans have large pouched bills that they use to scoop up fish from the water.

Plant stems and leaves grow toward light, which they need in order to make food by photosynthesis.

Investigation 1

Hiding from the Enemy

Materials

See advance preparation on page 56.

- student record sheet on page 59, reproduced for each student
- small envelopes
- watch or clock with a second hand
- graph paper

Steps to Follow

1. Explain the word **adaptation**—a physical structure or behavior that helps an organism survive in its habitat.

2. Write the terms **predator** and **prey** on the board. Explain that a predator is an animal that hunts for its food, and that prey are the animals caught. Ask students to name some predator-prey combinations (fox and rabbit; owl and mouse; lion and zebra).

3. Invite students to share what they know about **camouflage**. Tell them that they will do a simulation of predators hunting for prey to explore the adaptation of camouflage. Ask them how they think camouflage affects the ability of an animal to escape from predators. Have them write their predictions on their record sheets.

4. Divide the class into groups of five students. Make sure the number of students in each group is equal to the number of dot colors. Give each student two small envelopes. Station each group at a separate sheet of wrapping paper. Assign a different color dot to each student within a group.

5. Tell students that they are predators and the colored dots on the wrapping paper are their prey. When you say, "Go hunting!" they are to catch as many "prey animals" as they can. They may pick up only one dot at a time, using two fingers. They may only pick up the color assigned to them. Each dot is to be put into their envelope before they can pick up another one.

6. After students have "hunted" for 30 seconds, stop. Have them count the number of dots they collected and write it on their record sheets. Then have them put the dots into the second envelope. Continue in this way for at least five rounds.

7. Have students make bar graphs to show how many "prey animals" they caught in each round. Tell them to put the number of dots on the vertical axis and the rounds on the horizontal axis.

8. Tell students to find the total number of prey they caught. Then have each group make a bar graph of their totals. Tell them to put the number of dots on the vertical axis and the color on the horizontal axis.

9. Have groups compare their graphs. Discuss the similarities and differences. Challenge students to explain differences among the colors and the groups. Ask students to explain how camouflage is a useful adaptation for prey animals.

Name _____

Hiding from the Enemy

Prediction

1. How do you think camouflage helps a prey animal to survive?

_____

Procedure and Observations

2. Under "Observations," record what dot color you were assigned.

3. When your teacher says, "Go hunting!" pick up colored dots one at a time and put them in the envelope. Pick up only the color you were assigned.

4. Stop when the teacher indicates. Count your dots. Write the total on the chart.

5. Put these dots into a separate envelope.

6. Repeat Steps 2 through 4 four more times.

Dot Color: _____

	Round 1	Round 2	Round 3	Round 4	Round 5	Total
Number of Dots						

Conclusions

7. In your group, which color dots were the least likely to be picked up? Which were the most likely to be picked up?

_____

8. Which dots had the best camouflage? How did it affect the number picked up?

_____

9. How do you think camouflage helps prey animals to survive in nature?

_____

_____

Investigation 2

What Good Is a Thumb?

Materials

- student record sheet on page 61, reproduced for each student
- masking tape
- pencils
- jars with screw-on lids

Steps to Follow

1. Hold up one hand and wiggle all your fingers. Ask students how a human hand is different from a foot or from the foot of an animal such as a cat or dog. Explain that the human thumb is called an **opposable thumb** because it moves in the opposite direction to the other fingers.

2. Ask students what they think life would be like if people did not have opposable thumbs. Tell them that they will try to do various activities with their thumbs taped to their hands as a way to explore this idea. Invite them to predict what this will be like. Have them write their predictions on their record sheets.

3. Instruct students to work in pairs and take turns taping their partner's thumbs to the palms. Provide the materials they need to do the actions on the record sheet.

4. Challenge students to identify other tasks that they could not do, or could do only with great difficulty, without opposable thumbs. Invite them to discuss the value of the opposable thumb as an adaptation.

Follow-Up

Provide students with reference materials from the school or public library about monkey and ape behavior. Invite them to research how these animals make use of their opposable thumbs to survive in their habitats. Have students report their findings to the class.

Discuss the importance of the opposable thumb to the development of human civilization. Discuss inventions and cultural developments that would have been difficult or impossible without the use of the opposable thumb.

What Good Is a Thumb?

Prediction

1. What do you think it would be like to do various tasks without the use of your thumbs?

   _____

Procedure and Observations

2. Do each of the activities listed on the chart below using your hands normally. Observe and record how you do them.

3. Have your partner tape your thumbs to the palms of your hand.

4. Repeat each activity. Again observe and record how you do them.

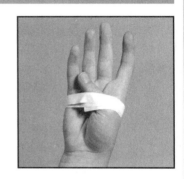

Activity	With Thumbs	Without Thumbs
picking up a pencil		
writing your name		
opening a jar		

Conclusions

5. What differences did you notice between doing the activities with and without the use of your thumbs?

   _____

   _____

6. In what ways is an opposable thumb a useful adaptation?

   _____

   _____

Concept **5** Living Things

Investigation 3
Blubber!

Materials

See advance preparation on page 56.

- student record sheet on page 63, reproduced for each student
- clock with second hand or stopwatches
- ice
- water
- large tubs
- newspapers
- paper towels
- disposable gloves
- shortening or petroleum jelly

Steps to Follow

1. Explain to students that some animals, including seals, whales, and penguins, have a thick layer of fat, or blubber, under their skin. Ask students to share what they know about the environment in which these animals live. Invite them to speculate how blubber functions as an adaptation.

2. Set large tubs of ice water on newspapers at stations around the classroom. Provide each group of students with a pair of disposable gloves, one of which is half filled with shortening or petroleum jelly. Place plenty of paper towels for cleanup at each station.

3. Tell students that they will put on the gloves, making sure that the hand in the glove with shortening is surrounded by fat, and they will then put both hands into the cold water at the same time. Have them predict how the fat will affect their ability to feel cold. Instruct them to write their predictions on their record sheets.

4. Provide a stopwatch or a clock with a second hand so that other students can time how long the student can keep his or her hands in the water. Tell them that if one hand gets too cold, they should remove it but leave the other hand in. Have students record the amount of time each hand stays in the water.

5. Instruct groups to make sure that each student gets a turn. Be sure to check if any students have allergies to the gloves that would prevent them from doing this activity. When necessary, add extra ice to keep the water very cold.

6. Invite students to describe the sensations they experienced. Ask them how quickly they felt discomfort in the hand not protected by fat.

7. Ask students to study their data. Challenge them to draw a conclusion about the function of blubber. Encourage students to explain why this is a useful adaptation to the environment of these animals.

Follow-Up

Provide reference materials about whales, seals, and penguins. Have students research their habitats and behaviors, and report their findings to the class.

Discuss how knowledge of the adaptation of a layer of fat in animals that live in cold climates might be used in developing adaptive equipment or clothing for extreme cold.

Name _____

Blubber!

Prediction

1. How do you think a layer of fat affects your ability to feel cold?

   _____

Procedure and Observations

2. Put one hand into a clean disposable glove. Put your other hand into a disposable glove that is half full of fat. Make sure the fat surrounds your hand.

3. Put both hands into ice water. Remove each hand when it becomes uncomfortable. You may remove one hand before the other.

4. Have your teammates time how long your hands are in the water.

5. Record the amount of time each hand stayed in the water.

6. Have each member of your group follow Steps 2 through 5.

Amount of Time Hands Are in Ice Water (sec.)

Student	Hand in Glove with Fat	Hand in Glove Without Fat

Conclusions

7. In your group, which hand could stay in the ice water longer?

   _____

8. What can you infer about the function of the fat?

   _____

9. What function do you think blubber serves in seals and other animals?

   _____

Investigation 4

Earthworm Behavior

Materials

See advance preparation on page 56.

- student record sheet on page 65, reproduced for each student
- aluminum foil
- cardboard boxes such as shoeboxes
- earthworms
- masking tape
- paper towels
- scissors
- water
- wooden sticks

Steps to Follow

1. Invite students to share what they know about earthworms. Discuss the habitat and needs of earthworms. Explain that in this activity they will investigate how earthworms respond to light and moisture. Invite students to predict how the earthworms will respond. Have them write their predictions on their record sheets.

2. Give each team a rectangular box. Have students cover the floor of the box with aluminum foil. Then have them cover half of the floor with wet paper towels and half with dry paper towels. Tell them to tape down the sides of the towels.

3. Have each team use a wooden stick to place two or three earthworms in the middle of the box on the border of the wet and dry towels. Provide a place where students can set their boxes aside for about an hour. Then have them observe their earthworms and record their observations on the record sheet.

4. Have students repeat the activity, this time spreading moist paper towels over the entire box. Instruct students to cut the lid in half and use it to cover one half of the box. Tell them to put the worms under the cut edge of the lid.

5. Make sure students wash their hands with hot water and soap after working with the worms.

6. Discuss how the earthworms responded to light and moisture. Challenge students to explain how these responses serve as useful adaptations to help earthworms stay alive in their environment.

Follow-Up

Invite students to suggest other animals that might respond to light or moisture. Discuss how this behavioral adaptation might help these animals. Encourage students to do library research about animals they think respond to these stimuli.

Name _____

Concept
5
Living Things

Investigation 4

Earthworm Behavior

Prediction

1. How do you think earthworms respond to light and moisture?

_____

Procedure and Observations

2. Cover the bottom of a box with aluminum foil. Tape it down.

3. Cover half of the bottom with wet paper towels and half with dry paper towels. Tape them down.

4. Put earthworms in the middle of the box. Cover the box. Set it aside.

5. After about an hour, observe the location of the worms.

6. Replace the dry towels with wet towels. Tape them down.

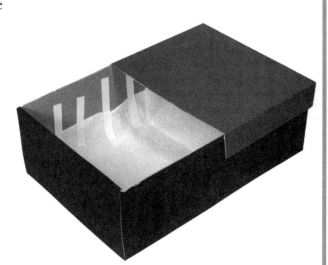

7. Cut the lid in half. Set it on the box.

8. Put earthworms in the middle of the box. Set it aside.

9. After about an hour, observe the location of the worms.

10. In which direction do the earthworms move when half the paper towels are dry and half are wet?

_____

11. In which direction do the earthworms move when half the box is in darkness and half is in light?

_____

Conclusions

12. What behavioral adaptations did you observe in the earthworms?

_____

13. How do you think these adaptations help the earthworms survive in their habitat?

_____

©2002 by Evan-Moor Corp.   65   Living Things • EMC 881

Investigation 5

Plant Behavior

Materials

See advance preparation on page 56.

- student record sheet on page 67, reproduced for each student
- clear jars
- paper towels
- soaked pinto beans
- water

Steps to Follow

1. Explain to students that behavior is a response to a change in the environment. Tell them that plants as well as animals can make such responses. Invite students to predict whether sprouting bean seeds respond to gravity and, if so, how they respond. Have them write their predictions on their record sheets.

2. Give each team five pinto bean seeds that have been soaked overnight. Tell them to moisten several paper towels, squeeze out the excess water, and fill a jar with the crumpled wet towels. Have them place the bean seeds between the wet towels and the side of the jar. On their record sheets, have students draw the appearance of the bean seeds.

3. Have students put the jars in a warm place out of direct sunlight. Instruct them to observe the seeds every day and to add a small amount of water if the paper towels begin to dry out. On the fourth day, have the students draw their seeds on their record sheets. (The roots will be growing toward the ground.)

4. Instruct students to turn their jar on its side. After two days, have them again observe the seeds and record their observations. (The roots will have turned to again grow toward the ground.)

5. Ask students to describe how the bean seedlings responded to gravity. Challenge them to explain how this behavior helps beans and other plants to survive.

Follow-Up

Have students turn their jars upside down. Encourage them to predict how the seedlings will grow.

Discuss with students the needs of plants. Invite them to speculate about what other behavioral adaptations plants might have. Challenge them to develop and run experiments to show these behaviors.

Concept
5
Living Things

Investigation 5

Plant Behavior

Prediction

1. Do you think bean seeds respond to gravity? If so, how?

_____

Procedure and Observations

2. Fill a jar with crumpled wet paper towels. Put five bean seeds between the towels and jar. Draw a picture of the seeds on the chart.

3. Put the jar in a warm place out of the sunlight. If the towels begin to dry out, add some water.

4. After four days, draw the seedlings.

5. Turn the jar on its side. After two days, draw the seedlings again.

Appearance of Bean Seeds/Seedlings

At Start	After Four Days	After Turning Jar

Conclusions

6. Describe the growth of the bean seedlings.

_____

7. How does the growth of the bean seedlings show evidence of an adaptation? How can this adaptation help keep the plants alive?

_____

_____

6

Energy from the Sun is transferred to living things.

Prepare in Advance

Investigation 1: Use ethyl alcohol in place of isopropyl alcohol if it is available, as it provides more distinctive results.

Investigation 2: If you wish, prepare the pigment extract from the geranium leaves ahead of time.

Investigation 3: For each team, prepare a set of animal cards with animals from your local area. In each set include at least 20 animals. There should be at least two herbivores, carnivores, omnivores, and insectivores. On each card, write the name of the animal. Leave room for a picture. Also prepare a set of label cards for each team that read: herbivore, carnivore, omnivore, and insectivore. Prepare a set of definition cards that read: feeds on plants, feeds on animals, feeds on a combination of plants and animals, and feeds on insects. You may want student volunteers to help you with this task.

Investigation 4: Create picture cards of plants and animals in your local area. Glue pictures to cards that are 5″ x 8″ (13 x 20 cm) or larger. Be sure to include green plants, various kinds of consumers, and decomposers. Make enough cards so that there is one for each student.

Teacher Information

Green plants transform the energy in sunlight to chemical energy (food) through the process of **photosynthesis.** In photosynthesis, light energy is absorbed by the green pigment in plants, **chlorophyll.** This energy is then used to fuel a complex set of chemical reactions. The summary of these reactions is $CO_2 + H_2O \rightarrow C_6H_{12}O_6 + O_2$, which means that carbon dioxide and water are converted to glucose and oxygen. A plant uses some of the glucose to provide energy for its own growth and maintenance. However, much of the glucose is converted to starch for storage. Both glucose and starch store chemical energy.

When an animal eats a plant, it takes in the chemical energy in the plant. The animal uses some of this energy to fuel its own reactions. Any excess energy is stored in the animal's tissues. Because energy is lost at every step along the **food chain,** there is a limit to the number of levels of consumers in an ecosystem. Generally, third- or fourth-level consumers are the top predators in a food web. **Decomposers** are a special kind of consumer. They break down the bodies of dead organisms and return nutrients, such as carbon and nitrogen, to the soil. Green plants take up these chemicals and use them for growth and maintenance.

A Food Web

The Sun is the source of energy
for the entire ecosystem.

Trees and grass are
producers. They contain the
green pigment chlorophyll.
Chlorophyll captures light
energy. Through
the process of
photosynthesis,
green plants
convert the energy
in sunlight to food.

Some
animals
are both
first- and
second-order consumers. They
are also omnivores, because
they eat both plant material
and animals.

First-order consumers
obtain their food,
and thus their
energy, from green
plants. They are also
known as herbivores
because their diet
consists only of plant
material.

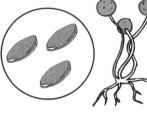

Second-order
consumers are
carnivores. They
obtain all of the
energy they need
by eating animals.

When a wolf eats
a deer (an herbivore),
it is a second-order
consumer. When it eats a
skunk, it is a third-order
consumer. It is always an
omnivore, and it is always
a predator. Since nothing in
the ecosystem eats the wolf,
it is a top consumer, or
top predator.

Decomposers break
down the remains of
all kinds of dead
organisms, from
plants to third-order
consumers. The
nutrients in the dead
bodies are then
returned to the soil,
where they can be
used again by plants.

Concept 6 Living Things

Investigation 1

The Producers

Materials

See advance preparation on page 68.

- student record sheet on page 71, reproduced for each student
- aluminum foil
- droppers or pipettes
- isopropyl alcohol
- geranium plant
- hot plate
- iodine
- large beaker
- paper clips
- paper towels
- petri dishes
- safety goggles
- saltine crackers
- tweezers

Steps to Follow

1. Invite students to speculate about the importance of sunlight to life on Earth. Remind them that plants convert the energy in sunlight into food, which they store as starch. Display a large, healthy geranium plant. Tell students they will investigate how light affects plants in general, and this plant in particular.

2. Have each team use paper clips to attach a small piece of foil to a different leaf of the plant. Make sure the foil covers only part of the leaf, but that no light reaches that part. Ask why the leaves are partially covered (to compare parts that receive light with parts that do not). Place the plant in bright light for at least four days.

3. Invite students to predict whether or not they will find starch in the geranium leaves, and if so, on which parts (covered or uncovered). Have them write their predictions on their record sheets.

4. Have each team remove a leaf from the plant, take off the foil, and give you the leaves. Wearing goggles, gently heat a beaker half full of isopropyl or ethyl alcohol. Put the leaves in the beaker and cook them several minutes until limp. Set them aside. ***Caution: Isopropyl alcohol is poisonous and highly flammable. Use with caution.***

5. Provide students with safety goggles. Give each team a cracker on a petri dish. Tell students that crackers contain starch. Instruct them to use a dropper to add a few drops of iodine to the cracker. How does iodine react to starch? (It turns dark blue or black.) Explain that when drops of iodine placed on food turn dark blue or black, it means the food contains starch. ***Caution: Iodine is poisonous; irritates skin, eyes, and nose; and stains clothes. Use with caution.***

6. Use tweezers to take the leaves out of the beaker and set them on paper towels. Give each team a leaf on a petri dish. Wearing safety goggles, have students use a dropper to completely cover the leaf with iodine. Tell them to wait several minutes and then record their observations. If no color change has occurred, have them observe the leaf again after about an hour. (The foil-covered part of the leaves should show no starch, while the exposed parts should turn black, indicating the presence of starch.)

7. Compare the results on the covered and uncovered parts of the leaf. Challenge students to explain any differences. (Only the portions of the leaves exposed to sunlight were able to undergo photosynthesis and produce starch.) How is this finding important?

The Producers

Prediction

1. What effect do you think light has on the presence of starch in leaves?

_____

Procedure and Observations

2. Attach a piece of foil to part of a leaf on the plant.

3. Add iodine to a cracker. Record your observations.

_____

_____

4. After four days, remove a leaf and the foil and have your teacher heat it in ethyl alcohol.

5. Put on your goggles. Cover the leaf with iodine. Describe how the leaf reacted to iodine.

The covered part:

_____

The uncovered part:

_____

Conclusions

6. How can you explain the reaction of iodine to different parts of the leaf?

_____

_____

7. What conclusions can you draw from your observations about the importance of light to plants?

_____

_____

Investigation 2
The Green in Plants

Materials

See advance preparation on page 68.

- student record sheet on page 73, reproduced for each student
- plastic cups
- geranium plant
- masking tape
- pipettes or eyedroppers
- rubbing alcohol
- safety goggles
- scissors
- sheet of white paper
- small plastic containers with lids
- strips of filter paper or blotter paper
- water
- water-soluble black markers

Steps to Follow

1. Hold up a leaf and a sheet of paper with a mark from a black marker. Ask what color each is. Tell students that they will investigate these colors more closely using **paper chromatography.** Explain that paper chromatography is used to separate the substances that make up a mixture. Discuss the meaning of the term **pigment** (a substance that gives a material its color). Invite students to predict what color pigments they think they will find in the ink and the leaf.

2. Give each team several leaves and a small plastic container with a lid. Have them tear the leaves into tiny pieces and put them in the container. Give students safety goggles. Instruct them to add about 1 cm of rubbing alcohol and tightly cover the container. Have them set their containers aside for two days. ***Caution: Isopropyl alcohol is poisonous and flammable.***

3. Give each team two strips of filter paper. Tell them to cut one end so it forms a point. On one strip, have students draw a line across the paper about 3 cm from the bottom with a water-soluble black marker. On the other, have them use a dropper to add a line of liquid from the container with the leaves. Make the line about 4 cm from the bottom. Instruct students to let the paper dry and then add another line of liquid on top of the first one. Have them do this four or five times.

4. Give each team two plastic cups. Have students wear safety goggles and add 1 cm of water to one cup and 1 cm of alcohol to the other cup, and label them accordingly. Instruct them to set their cups by a wall. Have them place the strip of filter paper with the marker on it so that the tip is in the water and tape the top end to the wall to hold it up. Have them set up the leaf solution paper in the cup with the alcohol in the same manner.

5. Allow 1 to 2 hours for the colors to separate. Once the colors have separated, tell students to remove the papers and let them dry.

6. Invite students to compare the results of the two setups. Ask how using the ink helped in understanding what happened with the leaves. (The ink setup showed that one color or pigment can actually be made of several colors.)

7. Identify the green leaf pigment as **chlorophyll.** Explain that light energy is captured by the chlorophyll. Ask why this is important (green plants use light energy to make food).

Name _____

The Green in Plants

Prediction

1. What color pigments do you think are found in ink and in a green leaf?

   _____

Procedure and Observations

2. Tear up the leaves and put them in the container. Wear safety goggles. Add 1 cm alcohol. Cover the container. Set it aside for two days.

3. Cut each strip of filter paper to form a point.

4. On one strip, draw a line 3 cm from the bottom (point) with a black marker. On the other strip, use a dropper to make a line of liquid from the container with the torn leaves. This line should be 4 cm from the bottom of the strip.

5. Fill one cup to 1 cm with water, and fill the other cup to 1 cm with alcohol. Label the cups accordingly.

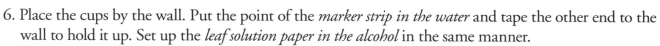

6. Place the cups by the wall. Put the point of the *marker strip in the water* and tape the other end to the wall to hold it up. Set up the *leaf solution paper in the alcohol* in the same manner.

7. After 1 to 2 hours remove the strips and observe them.

8. Describe what happened to the ink and the green liquid.

   _____

   _____

9. What colors could you see on each strip of filter paper?

   Ink _____ Green liquid _____

Conclusions

10. What color pigments are present in the leaf?

    _____

11. What role does chlorophyll play in a plant's life?

    _____

Concept 6 Living Things

Investigation 3

What Kind of -vore?

Materials

See advance preparation on page 68.

- student record sheet on page 75, reproduced for each student
- animal cards
- definition cards
- label cards
- resource materials on animals' feeding habits
- magazines with pictures of animals
- crayons or markers for drawing
- paste or glue
- scissors

Steps to Follow

1. Explain to students that animals must eat other organisms in order to obtain the energy they need to live. Tell them that animals can be divided into groups based on the types of organisms they eat.

2. Divide the class into teams of four. Give each team a set of four label cards and four definition cards. Challenge the students to match the correct definition with each label. Tell them that they can get hints from the names of the groups.

3. Discuss the students' decisions, making sure their matches are correct.

4. With the class, brainstorm a list of animals that live in nearby habitats. Write them on the board. Add any other animals you might have put on the animal cards.

5. Give each team a set of 20 different animal cards. Provide resources and instruct students to do research and find out what their animals look like and what they eat. Have them record their findings on their record sheets. Also have them cut out and paste a picture of each animal on the appropriate card, or draw a picture of each animal.

6. With the class, create a chart on the board to show what each animal eats.

7. Instruct the teams to use the information on the chart to group the animal cards under the correct set of label and definition cards.

8. Invite the teams to compare their results. Have them resolve any differences.

9. Have students compare the animals in each group. Invite them to explain how they are similar and how they are different. Provide them with a description of an animal. Challenge them to suggest the group it belongs to.

Follow-Up

Have groups of students create their own set of animal cards for a given ecosystem, such as a rainforest, desert, ocean, temperate forest, savannah, etc. Instruct them to make an answer key and trade card sets with another group.

Discuss which group humans fit into. (Most are omnivores.) Ask students which group they think a vegetarian would fit into (herbivore).

What Kind of -vore?

Procedure and Observations

1. Match each definition card with the correct label card.

2. Use reference materials to find out what the animals on your animal cards look like. On each animal card, draw a picture of the animal, or cut out and paste on a picture.

3. Find out what each animal eats. Record the information on the chart.

4. With the class, create a chart to show what each animal eats.

5. Place each animal card with the correct set of label and definition cards.

Name of Animal	What It Eats

Conclusion

6. How are the animals in each group alike? How are they different?

_____

_____

_____

_____

_____

_____

Investigation 4

The Web of Life

Materials

See advance preparation on page 68.

- student record sheet on page 77, reproduced for each student

- picture cards of plants and animals from the local area

- large yellow ball or circle of construction paper

- ball of yarn

Steps to Follow

1. Write the terms **producer, consumer,** and **decomposer** on the board. Discuss the meaning of each. Explain that various kinds of consumers exist. Tell students that an herbivore is a first-order consumer and that a carnivore that eats herbivores is a second-order consumer. Ask what they think a carnivore that eats carnivores is (third-order consumer). Explain that a decomposer is also a consumer.

2. Ask students what the ultimate source of energy for all producers and consumers is (the Sun). Tell them that they will model the passage of energy from the Sun through various kinds of organisms.

3. Have the students sit in a large circle. Give each student an animal card and have the students place the cards on the floor in front of them in full view.

4. Stand in the center of the circle and hold a ball of yarn and large yellow ball or paper circle. Ask students what the yellow ball represents (the Sun).

5. Holding firmly to the end of the yarn, toss the yarn ball to a student with a picture of a green plant. Instruct this student to pass the yarn ball to a person with a picture of an animal that might eat this green plant. Have students continue to pass the ball in this manner until it reaches an animal that is not eaten by anything else, such as an eagle. Have this person pass the yarn ball to a student with a decomposer card.

6. Explain to the students that they have just made a model food chain. Discuss how energy flows through the food chain. Ask students what the role of the producers is (to make food from the energy in sunlight).

7. Have the student with the decomposer card cut the yarn and then pass the yarn ball back to you. Repeat Step 5 several times.

8. Tell students they may pass the yarn ball to a student who had it on an earlier round. Then encourage this student to pass it to someone different than the last time. Point out that two food chains are now connected to form a food web.

9. Have students record two connecting food chains on their record sheets.

Follow-Up

Have students make their own model food chains. Have them paste pictures of the Sun and various organisms on a sheet of black construction paper and then connect the appropriate points with embroidery floss.

Name _____

The Web of Life

Concept **6** Living Things

Investigation 4

Procedure and Observations

1. Sit in a circle with your classmates. Place your animal card on the floor in front of you.

2. Create food chains by passing the ball of yarn from producer to first-order consumer to second-order consumer to third-order consumer (if they are shown) to decomposer.

3. Record two of the food chains made by your class.

Conclusions

4. What do the food chains you drew show?

_____

_____

5. What is the role of each organism (producer, consumer, or decomposer) in a food chain?

_____

_____

_____

©2002 by Evan-Moor Corp. 77 Living Things • EMC 881

Investigation 5

Nature's Decomposers

Materials

- student record sheet on page 79, reproduced for each student
- sliced bananas
- dry yeast
- plastic knives
- reclosable plastic bags
- teaspoons
- water
- masking tape
- marking pens

Steps to Follow

1. Ask students what organisms they think are considered decomposers. (Students may say earthworms, but actually earthworms are considered shredders, not decomposers. Bacteria and fungi are decomposers.) Challenge students to recall some kinds of fungi they have observed. Make sure they remember that yeast are fungi. Then ask students why they think decomposers are important. Accept all ideas.

2. Hold up a banana. Invite students to explain what effect they think decomposers would have on the banana. Have them write their predictions on their record sheets.

3. Have students put a slice of banana and 2 tsp. water into each bag. Have them add 1 tsp. of dry yeast to one bag. Have them seal the bags and use masking tape to identify the bag with the yeast. Instruct students to record the appearance of each banana on their record sheets. Provide a warm place for students to place their bags.

4. Each day for about a week, have students observe the bananas and record their observations. Have them compare the appearance of the fruit in the two bags. Challenge them to explain their observations.

5. Discuss the importance of decomposers to the ecosystem. Challenge students to imagine what the world would be like without decomposers.

Follow-Up

Have students bury a few slices of banana in the soil outside. Have them dig up the slices every few days and see what progress has been made in their decomposition. They may want to protect the bananas from consumers by covering them with a pot or other covering.

Name _____

Concept

6

Living Things

Investigation 5

Nature's Decomposers

Prediction

1. What effect do you think decomposers will have on a banana?

_____

Procedure and Observations

2. Put a slice of banana in each bag. Add 2 tsp. water to each bag.

3. Add 1 tsp. yeast to one bag. Mark it with masking tape.

4. Record the appearance of the bananas.

5. Place the bags in a warm place. Each day, observe the bananas and record your observations.

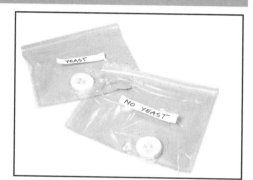

Day	Banana Alone	Banana with Yeast

Conclusions

6. What differences did you notice between the two bags?

_____

7. What is the effect of the yeast on the banana?

_____

8. How do decomposers help keep the ecosystem healthy?

_____